MOZART

COMPOSER CATS™

Written by Jeannine Kadow   Illustrated by Olo
Told by renowned conductor James Conlon

CHEVAL CREATIVE,LLC

PREMIERING SOON

CHEVAL TALES™
Stories that empower today's children.

Cheval Tale

The Nightmare Tree

A Princess in Blue Jeans

Waterman

Heart Song

My Hair Has a Head

The Lost Smile

The Sorcerer

The Happenstance Journey

COMPOSER CATS™

Mozart

Beethoven

Chopin

Gershwin

Bach

Brahms

Tchaikovsky

Rachmaninoff

Stravinsky

Paganini

Vivaldi

Ravel

Bartók

OPERA MICE™

The Barber of Seville

La Bohème

The Magic Flute

Aïda

Carmen

Rigoletto

Don Pasquale

Turandot

The Valkyrie

The Bat (Die Fledermaus)

La Traviata

The Marriage of Figaro

Il Trovatore

For James Conlon

M!

M for MEOW—for MOZART now.

Wolfgang Amadeus Mozart
wrote Music so classically sublime,
he became one of the great
Composer Cats of all time.

But once, long ago
in the cold Austrian night,
Mozart Cat slumped
in a musical blight.
He sat sadly at his piano,
paws on the keys,
playing seven note scales,
ABCDEFG, if you please.

His window was open
to a strong blustery wind
that ruffled his white wig
and chilled his chin.
"Where is my MUSIC?"
Mozart Cat cried,
as he leapt to the window
and jumped outside.

Mozart did not care that it was raining and dark.
The night hummed music: toad trills, a lone dog bark;
brooks babbled, leaves chattered, and snakes hissed a fine tune,
a symphony all: drums, flutes, and big bassoons.

"Where is my MUSIC?" Mozart yowled as he prowled,
while far off in the forest, a wild wolf howled.
His coat pockets were empty and ready to fill
with a new composition he knew would thrill
those kings and queens in lands near and far
who loved music composed by their composer star!

Mozart, overjoyed with his classical career,
listened for notes now with his perfectly pitched pink ear.
Our Composer Cat nosed through tight tangled brush,
and heard a bright G voiced by a red-legged thrush.
Mozart stalked that sound up a tree trunk,
but half way there bumped into a skunk!
Down, down, down, Mozart went as fast as he could,
Composer Cat claws gripping the hard tree wood.

Sweet-singing thrush winged through the night,
and landed on Mozart, quivering with fright.
The red-legged singer dropped the note from her beak
and flew off before the composer could eat.

Cats like to feast on mice and crunchy little birds,
but Mozart only wanted movements:
firsts, seconds and thirds.
(Don't forget the fourths, the final part in each!)
Mozart learned that when his Dad Cat would teach.
As young as a kitten age six, five, and four,
Mozart wrote notes at night for every new score.

Our composer now heard music
in the storm-battered sky,
night notes so sad
he pawed a tear from his eye.
The big, dark nocturnal commotion
pulsed through Mozart as musical emotion.

He knew that one night he would compose
a heart-wrenching piece,
a complex composition only
a master could release.
But our composer hunted now
for music quite light,
lilting, uplifting, and
danceably bright!

Mozart roamed the wilds for a special tone,
a lyrical line that tickled the bone.
He braved the shadowed dangers that wet forest held,
thankful he was not a housecat collared and belled.

In the dark, Mozart heard a foreboding deep beat,
a long, slow, harmonious suite
of sharp-toothed coons, bears, and bats.
So many critters hungry for CATS!

Thunder cracked, lightening forked, and dogs rained down,
but our composer pushed on with a fierce whiskered frown.
"Where is my MUSIC!" Mozart meowed in lament.
He KNEW it was out there and that his hunt was well spent.

Mozart Cat wandered, tail dragging, rain soaked and thin,
never expecting the first musical phrase to come from a fin.
Out in the water a fish leapt high in the air,
dancing with musical notes she wanted to share.

She had glittering scales, seven colors in all.
She flipped in fish frenzy and gave Mozart a call:
"Composer!" she sang. "The Night Music you seek,
rests here with me at the bottom of the creek.
"NOTES! A whole MOVEMENT I found;
the sweetest little night music around."

Fish tipped her tail and threw Mozart the first part
of our Composer Cat's new composition - his music, his art.
And just as Mozart caught the piece in his paw,
he rolled over and over in splendiferous awe!
For there in the forest, creatures convened
with music that was artfully polished and clean.

Tortoise groaned two bass notes BUH-BUM,
to Rabbit hopping with a fast high DEE-DEE-DUM.
Squirrel grabbed the notes and skittered away,
up the tree with a C sharp play
to Owl who who-whooed with a resounding D
that shook the earth, the pond, and the tree.

Fish quickly tossed more music to Mozart from her tail,
while snake snuck in and slither-zithered a scale.
Spider dropped down with an eight-legged divertimento,
a wild web of notes played in a perfectly timed tempo.
Spider dangled before Mozart on an F sharp thread,
playing the smallest of notes: "Tiny sixteenths!" he said.

A third movement came, confetti from the moon,
and fell to the ground not a moment too soon
for Spider's notes belonged in that part.
Cricket kicked in and leg-played with heart
the final fourth movement's opening phrase,
that told of the wonder of nights and not days.

Mozart grumbled and growled. Something was wrong.
A whole note was missing in this wonderful new song.
"An E!" he shouted, "after A, B, C, and D!"
Mozart then thrust up his arms in Composer Cat glee,
for right up there he saw a musician flying high
a raven winging through the cold night sky,
snatching the missing vowel
from the claws of a fierce feathered owl.
Raven dropped the E on a spiked porcupine's back
who marched to Mozart with prickly pride, the note intact.

Music spilled out of our Composer Cat's pockets,
while stars dropped the last notes like celestial rockets.
Mozart now knew he held his nocturnal dream –
one he would play on a stage of butter and cream.

"I need a violin," he anxiously announced,
a chance on which four night creatures instantly pounced.
Woodpecker drilled swiftly into a tree,
crafting a violin and bow with avian glee.
Chipmunk made strings from the whiskers of a rat,
which lovely shy Doe delivered to our cat.

Mozart gently put the instrument to his chin,
unaware that his first dancers would each sport a fin.
Fish waltzed across the water, high up on their tails,
joy radiating out from their colorful scales.

Composer Cat played in just the right key,
notes hitting as softly as a ripe buttery Brie.
This fresh piece was by far his most mellow.
If Mozart's new music had color, it would be yellow.

All through the forest
proud dwellers danced.
Frogs hip-hopped and
reindeer pranced.
Water-soaked ferrets
darted and twirled,
while stork and duck waltzed
and a swan pair whirled.

Even the trees danced, their long branches swayed
to the night music Mozart Cat so happily played.
Right up until dawn not a single note went missing,
Mozart finished to cheers and lots of kissing.

A little night music is
just right for a dance.
Try writing your own
when you have the chance.
For as our beloved
Mozart Cat knows,
even if you're a kitten,
you too can compose.

MOZART CAT™
COMPOSER NOTES

Learn something new!
It's the Cat's Meow!

Here are brief definitions of some of the important COMPOSER CATS™ words
in my musical mystery story. Come visit me at www.MozartCat.com.
We can play COMPOSER CATS™ games and go on more
mysterious musical adventures together!

AUSTRIA
The country in Europe where I was born on January 27, 1756.

BASS NOTES
The deepest, lowest sounds in music.

BASSOON
A really long musical instrument you play by blowing in and pressing
the special keys with your fingers.

BEAT
The length of time a note plays.

BLIGHT
Something that frustrates one's plans or ruins one's hopes.

BRIE
A type of soft, French cheese named after the town in France it is made in. It is very rich and creamy!

COMPOSE
To 'write' a piece of music by putting musical notes together.

COMPOSER
Someone who chooses the notes and how they are played so that you have a special song. Visit me on the Internet. I can teach YOU how to be a composer!

COMMOTION
An upsetting disturbance.

DRUM
A round musical instrument you play with sticks – or your bare hands! It is part of a family called 'percussion' instruments.

DAD CAT
My Father! His name was Johann (YO-HAN) Georg Leopold Mozart. He was a composer. He taught ME how to play and write music!

FELINE
Belonging to the CAT family. Lions, Tigers, and Jaguars are felines too.

FLUTE

A long musical instrument you play by blowing into it with your mouth and pressing keys with your fingers to make different musical sounds. (These keys are different from piano keys!) The flute is the OLDEST instrument in history! It is part of a family called 'woodwind' instruments.

FOREBODING

A sign of danger.

HARMONIOUS

A pleasing combination of musical notes.

HEART-WRENCHING

A very strong sad feeling.

MOVEMENT

Individual sections of a large composition of music. The first movement is the first section of the musical composition. The second movement comes after the first. The third comes after the second. And the fourth comes after the third. They are like chapters in a book.

MUSICAL SCALES

A series of seven notes played in order.

NOCTURNAL
Something that happens at NIGHT!

PIANO KEYS
The part you press on the piano with your finger that makes the piano 'play' a note. There are 52 wide white keys and 36 narrow black keys – 88 keys all together. Each key makes a different sound.

PITCH
One of the three major elements of sound. You cannot have music without having pitch.

SCORE
The written pages of music notes that show all the parts the instruments play in a piece of music.

TORTOISE
A kind of turtle.

VIOLIN
A stringed instrument played with a bow.

MUSICAL GAMES

MOZART CAT composed these games for you!
You do not need an instrument - just your imagination.

A LITTLE NIGHT MUSIC

At night, listen to the sounds all around you. What do you hear? Crickets chirping? Sirens screaming? Horns honking? A cat meowing? A train rumbling? Wind blowing hard? Rain falling fast? Hail falling hard? A dog barking? River water rushing over boulders? Ocean waves pounding the shore? Mozart Cat hears music in everything around him. Listen like you are Mozart Cat, and then sing a sound for each night sound you hear.

Example: Eu-Urp, Woo-Woo, Uhr-Uhr, Onk-Onk, Meowww-Meowww.

That is your own night music song!

MOZART MAKES ME FEEL

Mozart Cat expresses many emotions in his musical mystery. When he can't find the notes he needs for his new piece of music at his piano, he feels SAD. Then, when he goes into the dark forest looking for the notes, he is SCARED. But he does not give up. He continues on with his search, feeling DETERMINED and BRAVE.

When he has all the notes he needs, Mozart Cat is HAPPY. He plays the new music on his new violin feeling JOYFUL. Go through the story and look carefully at Mozart Cat's face. Think of a time when YOU felt like Mozart. If you turn all of those feelings into music, you will have a very important song: YOUR song.

You can be a Composer Cat too!

MOZART CAT DANCE

The CD with this book has a track of Mozart's music. Parts of it are like the stormy night in the forest. Other parts are from Mozart's new piece of dance music. Play it and listen for the difference. Make up a dance, expressing how the music makes you feel with your movements.

Dance like a storm!

Dance with joy!

Compose a name for your dance and then make up a new dance all over again!

CAT SCALE SONG

Cats love to climb and Composer Cats are no exception.

You can climb like a Composer Cat! There are seven different notes in a music scale. When you play or sing a scale, you always go one step higher to end on the note you began with. Listen to the piano scale on the CD.

Sing along with each note: do, re, mi, fa, so, la, ti, do.

Sing in reverse when the scale goes down: do, ti, la, so, fa, mi, re, do.

The next time you go up a staircase, imagine the steps are piano keys and sing the scale: do, re, mi, fa, so, la, ti, do.

Sing the scale as you go down the stairs, one note for each step:
do, ti, la, so, fa, mi, re, do.

MUSICAL COLOR

Music makes you feel. Some music makes you so happy you want to dance. Some music makes you want to just sit quietly and look at the sky. Colors do too. Certain colors make you want to jump up and down with joy. Other colors make you want to write a poem.

Using markers, pencils, or crayons, draw pictures of musical notes in different colors. Look at each colored note carefully. How does it make you feel? Sing the name of the color out loud. If RED makes you happy, sing it in a happy way. Once you have a sound for each colored note, mix them all up and sing your very own COLOR SONG!

Even if you are a kitten, you too can compose.

GREAT LEAPING FISH!

Draw a FISH. Imagine your fish lives in Mozart Cat's forest stream. Color the scales seven different colors. (A fish scale is different from a music scale. Words can sound and look the same but mean different things. Language is fun!) When you finish, make up a song for your fish and sing it.

You have your very own Composer Cat Fish Song!

CONTRIBUTORS

JEANNINE KADOW
Writer/Creator

An internationally acclaimed suspense writer, Jeannine writes a new movement of literature for children with her musical mysteries featuring the world's most beloved composers as COMPOSER CATS™. She began her professional career as a broadcast journalist and moved on to executive positions at Warner Brothers. She left Warner Brothers to live in France, specializing in international film and television content creation. Jeannine returned to the U.S. full time to build CHEVAL CREATIVE, a legacy children's entertainment entity devoted to delivering entertainment for children that has cultural depth and substantive meaning. Her principal residence is now in Aspen, Colorado.

ALEXANDER 'OLO' SCORZYNSKI
Illustrator

Alexander "OLO" Sroczynski was born in Poland. His illustrations have been published internationally. OLO has created more than fifty animated films. His children's books showcase his unique style and timeless artistic quality. OLO's book, created with Whoopi Goldberg, "Whoopi's Big Book Of Manners," won the NAACP Image Award. OLO lives in Connecticut.

JAMES CONLON
Narrator
World Renowned Conductor

James Conlon is Music Director of the LA Opera, the Ravinia Festival, and the Cincinnati May Festival. One of today's most recognized conductors, he has led more than 250 performances at the Metropolitan Opera, has appeared as guest conductor with virtually every major North American and European orchestra, and has served as Principal Conductor of the Paris National Opera, General Music Director of the City of Cologne, Germany, and Music Director of the Rotterdam Philharmonic. He is known for his work with young musicians and for his efforts to raise public consciousness to the significance of composers whose lives and compositions were suppressed by the Nazi regime, for which he received a Crystal Globe Award from the Anti-Defamation League. Among his numerous citations and awards, he is the recipient of two Grammy Awards, an Opera News Award, and is a Classical Music Hall of Fame inductee. Mr. Conlon was named an Officier de L'Ordre des Arts et des Lettres by the French Government in 1996, and in 2004 was promoted to Commander. In 2002, James Conlon received France's highest distinction from President Jacques Chirac—the Légion d'Honneur.

NINO RAJACIC
Composer/Arranger
Music for COMPOSER CATS™ MOZART CD

Nino is a Serbian conductor, freelance composer, and sound designer. He is a classically trained composer graduated from the Academy of Arts at the University of Novi Sad, specializing in music theory and pedagogy. As one of the co-founders of 3 Peak Audio, Nino has been working extensively on producing music and sound for games, TV, film, and multimedia with credits in over 30 projects worldwide including clients such as HBO Networks, Sony Pictures, and ABC Networks.